A Message From the Author

So, I thought you should know why I wrote this book.

Since the beginning of time, parents have felt a responsibility to teach their children the basic skills needed to survive in a world filled with never-ending challenges...like starting a fire before there were matches, chiseling a wheel from stone when the chisel hadn't been invented, or skinning a bear to make a blanket once you realized you couldn't figure out how to start a fire.

Fast forward to today. For most of us, from the moment we become a parent, our intention is to teach our kids the basic skills of life. However, all too often there's a huge gap between intention and reality. I've written this book to help fill that gap.

Here are a few things this book is and a few things it's not.

This is not a "reading" book. It is a guide and a journal filled with "check-lists" that help track your progress as you teach your child important basic life skills.

It's not a "how to" book that teaches the details of each life lesson. That's what the internet and reference libraries are for.

It's not about hugging or loving your kids, or about providing for their everyday needs of food, shelter, and clothing and it's not about having that talk about the "birds and the bees" when the time is right..

It's not about teaching your kids how to tie their shoelaces or putting a band aid on a boo-boo...nope! It is about things like sewing on a button, cooking a chicken, and unclogging a drain.

This guide is about passing on common, every-day, basic knowledge from one generation to the next. It is about you sharing your experience and wisdom that have been honed by years of trial and error.

I've never written a book like this. But, I have raised two boys and two girls and lived to tell about it. Everything I'm sharing comes from that experience and my battles from the "school of hard knocks." I've lost some, won some, and at other times gotten beat up so badly that all I wanted to do was throw in the towel.

Before any of my kids were born, I intended to be the best dad this world's ever seen. That didn't work out exactly the way I'd drawn it up in my mind. I wasn't a terrible dad. I just wasn't as good as I could've been when it came to teaching my kids these simple, basic life skills.

Patience wasn't my long suit so my kids ended up getting the fuzzy end of the sucker. The fact is, it's just a lot easier to get things done if you don't include your kids, right?

I mean, you can bake a batch of peanut butter cookies and be done in twenty minutes. But, mix in a five year old and it can take you three hours just to clean up the mess they've made. The problem is, they never learned how to bake a cookie. I hope you caught that! Understanding that cookie thing is a really big deal.

To make things worse, here's what's happened: Somewhere along the line, we lost a bunch of electives in our school system and it just sort of snuck up on us. All of a sudden, classes like home-ec, auto shop, cooking, woodworking, driver's-ed, and a number of other life skill instructions just disappeared. We woke up one day and found ourselves with a giant hole in the "equipping our kids for the future" options that were always a part of general education.

Couple that with dual-income households where both parents are at work, increased homework loads for the student, then add in sports, social commitments, and dozens of other activities and obligations screaming out for our attention and... BAM...there's hardly the time or energy left to replace what our kids lost in school.

As I look back, I believe I would have done better if I'd had a plan...a program or system, a collection of checklists like this to work with. That would have helped me teach my kids these basic life skills instead of hoping they'd somehow get "taught or caught" by accident.

Knock, Knock...You've got to listen to me here...I'm trying to help you. I'm trying to save you from waking up some night in a cold sweat realizing that the first time your kids try to change a light switch it could be a life or death experience because you never taught them the difference between the white wire, the black wire, and the green wire.

Now, I wasn't always the only problem. For years, my wife insisted I cut the kid's meat for them because she was terrified at what might happen if they touched a sharp knife. As a result, our oldest daughter grew up actually having to ask her dates to cut her steak for her. To this day she still suffers from the embarrassment.

Because of my wife's fears, we overprotected our kids. Our youngest son believed that if he ever pulled the trigger on a circular saw he'd be dismembered and left to bleed out in our garage. He still has a nervous reaction when he hears the sound of a power tool and he thinks Home Depot is a haunted house.

Our youngest daughter has no idea that a "'jack" is used to change a tire or that a "phillips" is a screwdriver. To her, they're just a couple of boy's names.

Here's the trickle-down effect. Our oldest son got a call from one of his daughters the first time she went to fill her car with gas. When she called she was in a panic because the nozzle wouldn't fit into the gas tank. Needless to say, this happened because her dad never took the time to teach her that basic life skill about the "green hose."

So, here's how this works.

At an appropriate age, when you're getting ready to tackle one of the items on these "checklists"...include your child...simple as that! Let them watch, let them participate, and let them learn.

Tell them stories of how you learned to do what your doing, who taught you, where the recipe came from, and what the house smelled like when grandma made that special holiday meal. Make sure they get to pound some nails, change the vacuum cleaner bag, mix the cake batter...and make real sure they get to lick the spoon.

So, there you have it. I've written this book with the hope that it'll help you be better at all this than I was. I've written it with the hope that it'll make it easier for you than it was for me. My hope is that your children will benefit from it and become better adults (and better parents too, if they choose to one day have children of their own).

Disclosure...I've also written it for my own selfish benefit...believing that if, during my lifetime, I help one person do it better than I did it'll somehow give meaning to my own failures and make me feel better before I die.

Full disclosure...I've also written this in the hope that I can sell enough of them to offset the enormous costs of helping put eight grandchildren through college.

One of my favorite things about this guide is that some lessons will be learned by BOTH you and your child. Let's face it, sometimes, one of the reasons we don't teach our kids something is because we don't have a clue about how to do it ourselves.

There's no particular order that the life lessons must be completed and there are no time limits. There are no grades and no "pass" or "fail". Every child will benefit from these lessons at *their* own pace and at *their* age appropriate time. This guide is about the journey and it's a journey that'll be years in the making.

Very few kids, if any, will complete every life skill in this guide before they leave home. That doesn't mean you've failed...not by a long shot. But, there's a real good chance that you'll have taught your kids more using this guide than you would have without it.

It serves as a future reminder of where you started, how far you've come, and how much you accomplished.

And finally, keep this in mind...the better your kids do in life...the better they can take care of you in the future.

Enjoy the journey and have fun!

Norm Whan

A Guide To Your Guide

Your guide starts with a **"Dedication Page."** This is an opportunity for you to share with your child what your thoughts were when you chose to start this journey with them.

You're now on to the **"Checklists"** that make up the vast majority of this guide. Every checklist has the name of the basic life skill and a place for a check mark when the lesson has been completed.

In addition, there's a place for the date it was completed, a place to record the child's age at that time, and a place for you and your child to initial.

You can even customize your guide. There are three "FILL-IN" lines at the end of each category for you to add your favorite basic life skills and there are four "FILL-IN" pages for you to add new categories.

The **"NOTES"** section is a space for me to share a few thoughts about one or more of the skills on that page.

The **"MEMORIES,"** on the back of each checklist page, allows everyone involved in teaching the life skills to share their experience and record their favorite memories. In the long run, that section may be the most valuable thing this guide records for you and your child.

You don't have to be the only teacher. Use the skill sets of other family or friends. If grandpa is a plumber...let him teach some of the plumbing skills.

Your guide also includes a **"Certificate of Accomplishment."** It can be signed by everyone that was involved in the process over the years. When your child is ready to leave home, pass the guide on to them to be continued and completed in the future. It'll end up being a keepsake.

All of that because you taught them how to change a tire...and lots, lots more.

Dedicated To

On this _____ day of _____ in the year of _____

Signatures

133 Basic Life Skills

REMEMBER

This is not a **"HOW TO DO IT"** book...this is a **"YOU SHOULD DO IT"** book.

 1-Auto

 9-Grocery Shopping

 17-Painting

 2-Baking

 10-Hand Tools and Power Tools

 18-Pet Care

 3-Banking

 11-House Cleaning

 19-Plumbing

 4-Bathrooms

 12-Kitchen

 20-Safety

 5-Build Something

 13-Knots

 21-Sewing and Mending

 6-Chores

 14-Laundry

 22-Small Appliances

 7-Cooking

 15-Lawn and Landscaping

 23-Time Management

 8-Electrical

 16-Maintenance

Your journey is about to begin.

HAVE A GREAT TIME!

Auto

"Lots of people remember spending time in the driveway with their parents, working on the family car. For many of you dads and moms out there, the opportunity to teach your kids about car repairs is a rite of passage. Plus, it builds great memories."
– Erich Reichert – NAPA Know How Blog

AUTO CHECKLIST

Change A Tire	Date _____	Age ___	Initial ___	Initial ___
Pump Gas	Date _____	Age ___	Initial ___	Initial ___
Oil Change and Check All Other Fluids	Date _____	Age ___	Initial ___	Initial ___
Tire Inspection (Including the Spare)	Date _____	Age ___	Initial ___	Initial ___
Jumper Cables and Battery Maintenance	Date _____	Age ___	Initial ___	Initial ___
Keep Vehicle Clean & Clutter Free	Date _____	Age ___	Initial ___	Initial ___
Snow Chains & De-Ice Windows	Date _____	Age ___	Initial ___	Initial ___
Record Keeping	Date _____	Age ___	Initial ___	Initial ___
_____	Date _____	Age ___	Initial ___	Initial ___
_____	Date _____	Age ___	Initial ___	Initial ___
_____	Date _____	Age ___	Initial ___	Initial ___

NOTES

The automobile is the second largest financial investment most people will make. The quality care and maintenance of it is critical to getting the highest return on that investment.

Record keeping starts with the purchase agreement, title, registration, and insurance. It includes every receipt and every penny spent for maintenance from day one and should be kept in chronologic order. Records should also include any accidents or cosmetic repairs or enhancements made. In most cases, this history will increase your car's resale value.

1

Auto

MEMORIES

_____
_____
_____
_____
_____
_____
_____
_____
_____
_____
_____
_____
_____
_____
_____
_____
_____
_____
_____
_____
_____
_____
_____
_____
_____
_____
_____
_____

Baking

"Baking...it can get messy and chaotic, but wow, the memories you're creating together! They're so worth it."
– Cafémom.com

BAKING CHECKLIST

A Batch of Cookies   Date _____ Age ___ Initial ___ Initial ___

Bake and Ice a Layer Cake   Date _____ Age ___ Initial ___ Initial ___

Bake and Ice Cupcakes   Date _____ Age ___ Initial ___ Initial ___

A Pie   Date _____ Age ___ Initial ___ Initial ___

Muffins   Date _____ Age ___ Initial ___ Initial ___

A Pizza   Date _____ Age ___ Initial ___ Initial ___

Brownies   Date _____ Age ___ Initial ___ Initial ___

_____   Date _____ Age ___ Initial ___ Initial ___

_____   Date _____ Age ___ Initial ___ Initial ___

_____   Date _____ Age ___ Initial ___ Initial ___

NOTES

No matter what you mix, make sure your kid gets to lick the spoon, the beaters, and the bowl! They'll never forget the experience. Yummy!

2

Baking

MEMORIES

_____
_____
_____
_____
_____
_____
_____
_____
_____
_____
_____
_____
_____
_____
_____
_____
_____
_____
_____
_____
_____
_____
_____

Banking

"If you don't teach your kids how to manage money, somebody else will. And that's not a risk you want to take."
– Dave Ramsey – Author and Founder of Financial Peace University

BANKING CHECKLIST

Open a Savings Account   Date _____ Age ___ Initial ___ Initial ___

Open a Checking Account   Date _____ Age ___ Initial ___ Initial ___

Manage Your Accounts   Date _____ Age ___ Initial ___ Initial ___

Make a Budget   Date _____ Age ___ Initial ___ Initial ___

Use an ATM   Date _____ Age ___ Initial ___ Initial ___

Use Online Banking   Date _____ Age ___ Initial ___ Initial ___

_____   Date _____ Age ___ Initial ___ Initial ___

_____   Date _____ Age ___ Initial ___ Initial ___

_____   Date _____ Age ___ Initial ___ Initial ___

NOTES

When it's time to open an account for your child, be sure to let them interact with the bankers.

Let them discuss their goals and ask questions.

Let your children actually handle the cash for deposits and from withdrawals.

Help them establish and achieve short-term and long-term financial goals.

3

Banking

MEMORIES

_____
_____
_____
_____
_____
_____
_____
_____
_____
_____
_____
_____
_____
_____
_____
_____
_____
_____
_____
_____
_____
_____
_____
_____
_____

Bathrooms

"What could be more useless than a man who couldn't fix a dripping faucet...fundamentally useless."
– Don DeLillo – White Noise

BATHROOMS CHECKLIST

Use a Toilet Plunger and a Sink Plunger   Date _____ Age ___ Initial ___ Initial ___

Replace Flushing System   Date _____ Age ___ Initial ___ Initial ___

Change and Clean a Shower Head   Date _____ Age ___ Initial ___ Initial ___

Replace a Toilet Seat   Date _____ Age ___ Initial ___ Initial ___

_____   Date _____ Age ___ Initial ___ Initial ___

_____   Date _____ Age ___ Initial ___ Initial ___

_____   Date _____ Age ___ Initial ___ Initial ___

NOTES

Yes! There is a difference between a toilet plunger and a sink plunger.

Everyone in the household, including kids at the appropriate age, should know where the inside and outside water shutoff valves are and how to operate them.

Coupled with quick action, this knowledge can be the difference between a small issue and a major mop–up.

4

Bathrooms

MEMORIES

_____
_____
_____
_____
_____
_____
_____
_____
_____
_____
_____
_____
_____
_____
_____
_____
_____
_____
_____
_____
_____
_____
_____
_____
_____
_____
_____
_____

Build Something

*"Kids today, their dream isn't to build something,
it is to buy something."*

Chip Foose – Auto Designer – Author – Actor

BUILD SOMETHING CHECKLIST

A Stained or Painted Box With   Date _____ Age ___ Initial ___ Initial ___
A Hinged Lid And Handles

Birdhouse or a Birdfeeder   Date _____ Age ___ Initial ___ Initial ___

Dog House   Date _____ Age ___ Initial ___ Initial ___

Pinewood Derby Car   Date _____ Age ___ Initial ___ Initial ___

Models   Date _____ Age ___ Initial ___ Initial ___

Assemble/Maintain A Bike   Date _____ Age ___ Initial ___ Initial ___

_____   Date _____ Age ___ Initial ___ Initial ___

_____   Date _____ Age ___ Initial ___ Initial ___

_____   Date _____ Age ___ Initial ___ Initial ___

NOTES

A project worked on with your child accomplishes more than just building something together.

It introduces your kids to the safe use of tools and strengthens their large and small motor skills.

Starting out with a 4' X 8' sheet of plywood and creating a box with a hinged lid, handles on both ends, and is then stained or painted will introduce the use of nearly all basic tools.

5

Build Something

MEMORIES

Chores

"If you want to change the world, start off by making your bed. If you make your bed every morning, you will have accomplished the first task of the day. Making your bed will reinforce the fact that the little things in life matter."
– William H. McRaven, Former United States Navy Admiral

CHORES CHECKLIST

Make Your Bed Every Day   Date _____ Age ___ Initial ___ Initial ___

Keep Your Room Neat   Date _____ Age ___ Initial ___ Initial ___

Pick Up After Yourself   Date _____ Age ___ Initial ___ Initial ___

Take the Trash Out   Date _____ Age ___ Initial ___ Initial ___

Iron Your Own Clothes   Date _____ Age ___ Initial ___ Initial ___

_____   Date _____ Age ___ Initial ___ Initial ___

_____   Date _____ Age ___ Initial ___ Initial ___

_____   Date _____ Age ___ Initial ___ Initial ___

NOTES

Start your child early and be consistent.

Doing their chores regularly is one of the first steps to building responsible habits.

Other chores are included in other categories.

Chores

MEMORIES

_____
_____
_____
_____
_____
_____
_____
_____
_____
_____
_____
_____
_____
_____
_____
_____
_____
_____
_____
_____
_____
_____
_____
_____

Cooking

"Children learn lifetime skills by practicing basic math skills such as counting, weighing, measuring, tracking time, and they also gain social skills by working together and communicating in the kitchen."
– Mary Ann McFarland – Author of "Cooking With Kids in School; Why It's Important"

COOKING CHECKLIST

Fry – Scramble – Hard Boil an Egg	Date _____	Age ___	Initial ___	Initial ___
Prepare a Fish Entrée	Date _____	Age ___	Initial ___	Initial ___
Roast a Chicken	Date _____	Age ___	Initial ___	Initial ___
Prepare and Cook Raw Vegetables	Date _____	Age ___	Initial ___	Initial ___
Cook a Steak	Date _____	Age ___	Initial ___	Initial ___
Mix a Hearty Salad	Date _____	Age ___	Initial ___	Initial ___
Make Spaghetti and Meat Balls	Date _____	Age ___	Initial ___	Initial ___
Meatloaf & Mashed Potatoes & Gravy	Date _____	Age ___	Initial ___	Initial ___
Prepare A Complete Family Meal	Date _____	Age ___	Initial ___	Initial ___
_____	Date _____	Age ___	Initial ___	Initial ___
_____	Date _____	Age ___	Initial ___	Initial ___
_____	Date _____	Age ___	Initial ___	Initial ___

NOTES

Who knew that cooking and baking could improve your kid's skills in reading, math, geometry, as well as their overall health?

Think about it: Take 1/4 cup of orange juice, 1/2 a teaspoon of salt, 1 tablespoon of oil, 1 cup of milk, an 8x10 pan, cut it into squares or make a triangle out of the dough.

According to some research, kids who cook eat more fruits, vegetables, and other healthy foods and have a better understanding of nutritional health.

7

Cooking

MEMORIES

Electrical

"Electricity can be dangerous. My nephew tried to stick a penny into a light plug. Whoever said a penny doesn't go far didn't see him shoot across the floor. I told him he was grounded!"
– Tim Allen, Comedian, Actor, Author

ELECTRICAL CHECKLIST

Find and Use the Circuit Breaker   Date _____ Age ___ Initial ___ Initial ___

Replace a Light Switch   Date _____ Age ___ Initial ___ Initial ___

Replace a Wall Plug   Date _____ Age ___ Initial ___ Initial ___

Strip and Splice Wires   Date _____ Age ___ Initial ___ Initial ___

Replace Light Bulbs   Date _____ Age ___ Initial ___ Initial ___

_____   Date _____ Age ___ Initial ___ Initial ___

_____   Date _____ Age ___ Initial ___ Initial ___

_____   Date _____ Age ___ Initial ___ Initial ___

NOTES

SAFETY! SAFETY! SAFETY!

This is definitely not the place to learn from your mistakes.

Here is one of those areas that can end up "sparking" a high level of interest and may end up becoming a lifelong career.

8

Electrical

MEMORIES

_____
_____
_____
_____
_____
_____
_____
_____
_____
_____
_____
_____
_____
_____
_____
_____
_____
_____
_____
_____
_____
_____
_____
_____
_____
_____
_____
_____

Grocery Shopping

"The odds of going to the store for a loaf of bread and coming out with only a loaf of bread are three billion to one."
– Erma Bombeck, Author, Writer

GROCERY SHOPPING CHECKLIST

Prepare a Grocery List   Date _____ Age ___ Initial ___ Initial ___

Shop and Compare Prices   Date _____ Age ___ Initial ___ Initial ___

Help Carry and Put Groceries Away Date _____ Age ___ Initial ___ Initial ___

Understand Nutrition Panels   Date _____ Age ___ Initial ___ Initial ___

Understand "Use By" and "Expiration" Date _____ Age ___ Initial ___ Initial ___

Learn Safe Food Storage   Date _____ Age ___ Initial ___ Initial ___

_____   Date _____ Age ___ Initial ___ Initial ___

_____   Date _____ Age ___ Initial ___ Initial ___

_____   Date _____ Age ___ Initial ___ Initial ___

NOTES

This list prepares your child for their adventures in the kitchen.

Adding a "budget" for a shopping trip increases the awareness of price comparisons.

Grocery Shopping

MEMORIES

_____
_____
_____
_____
_____
_____
_____
_____
_____
_____
_____
_____
_____
_____
_____
_____
_____
_____
_____
_____
_____
_____
_____
_____

Hand Tools and Power Tools

"Giving children the opportunity to use real tools alongside you gives them confidence, tunes fine motor skills and makes important life connections. Having the confidence to use simple tools is a gift that carries them though life."

– Hillary – steadymom.com

HAND TOOLS AND POWER TOOLS CHECKLIST

Put a Basic "Kid's Tool Box" Together   Date _____ Age ___ Initial ___ Initial ___

Hammers, Screwdrivers, Wrenches   Date _____ Age ___ Initial ___ Initial ___

Pliers, Cutters, Tape Measure   Date _____ Age ___ Initial ___ Initial ___

Hand Saws and Power Saws   Date _____ Age ___ Initial ___ Initial ___

Power Drills and Power Sanders   Date _____ Age ___ Initial ___ Initial ___

Safety Goggles   Date _____ Age ___ Initial ___ Initial ___

_____   Date _____ Age ___ Initial ___ Initial ___

_____   Date _____ Age ___ Initial ___ Initial ___

_____   Date _____ Age ___ Initial ___ Initial ___

NOTES

Put together a "kid's tool box" that's all their own. Fill it with appropriate size tools to make it easy for them to use.

Teach them to respect, clean and care for their tools. "Hammer" safety tips into them.

10

Hand Tools and Power Tools

MEMORIES

House Cleaning

"Cleaning with kids in the house is like brushing your teeth while eating Oreos."
-Somecards

HOUSE CLEANING CHECKLIST

Vacuuming   Date _____ Age ___ Initial ___ Initial ___

Dusting   Date _____ Age ___ Initial ___ Initial ___

Mop Floors   Date _____ Age ___ Initial ___ Initial ___

Wash Windows Inside and Outside   Date _____ Age ___ Initial ___ Initial ___

Clean Sinks, Showers and Tubs   Date _____ Age ___ Initial ___ Initial ___

Clean Mirrors   Date _____ Age ___ Initial ___ Initial ___

_____   Date _____ Age ___ Initial ___ Initial ___

_____   Date _____ Age ___ Initial ___ Initial ___

_____   Date _____ Age ___ Initial ___ Initial ___

NOTES

Playing with water and soap bubbles is always fun for kids. Cleaning sinks and tubs and mopping floors lets them splash a little while they clean a little. Don't miss this opportunity to catch them having fun while they're learning.

A vacuum cleaner is a fascinating "monster" with all those hoses and gadgets and the noise that it makes. Let your kids put the "pieces" together and watch the "magic" of picking up a Cheerio with a wave of the wand.

If you're lucky and have enough dust, kids can have fun writing their name or drawing a picture or design before they wipe the surface clean. It's like having a free Etch-A-Sketch.

House Cleaning

MEMORIES

_____
_____
_____
_____
_____
_____
_____
_____
_____
_____
_____
_____
_____
_____
_____
_____
_____
_____
_____
_____
_____
_____
_____
_____
_____
_____
_____

Kitchen

"Everybody wants to save the earth. Nobody wants to help mom do the dishes."
–P.J. O'Rourke

KITCHEN CHECKLIST

Learn How to Extinguish a Grease Fire Date _____ Age ___ Initial ___ Initial ___

Clean a Sink Trap Date _____ Age ___ Initial ___ Initial ___

Load and Operate a Dishwasher Date _____ Age ___ Initial ___ Initial ___

Clean the Stove and Oven Date _____ Age ___ Initial ___ Initial ___

Clean and Organize the Refrigerator Date _____ Age ___ Initial ___ Initial ___

Clean and Organize Cupboards Date _____ Age ___ Initial ___ Initial ___

Replace Refrigerator Water Filter Date _____ Age ___ Initial ___ Initial ___

_____ Date _____ Age ___ Initial ___ Initial ___

_____ Date _____ Age ___ Initial ___ Initial ___

_____ Date _____ Age ___ Initial ___ Initial ___

NOTES

Everyone in the household, including kids at the appropriate age, should know where the fire extinguishers are and how to operate them.

It is important that fire extinguishers are regularly serviced and maintained.

For safety, kids at the appropriate age should know where and how to operate gas and water shutoff valves, especially in the kitchen.

12

Kitchen

MEMORIES

_____
_____
_____
_____
_____
_____
_____
_____
_____
_____
_____
_____
_____
_____
_____
_____
_____
_____
_____
_____
_____
_____
_____

Knots

"Tying a knot is one of the most important skills that everybody should learn. It does not only help us in many practical ways, but it can save lives during an emergency."
– IdeaHacks.com

KNOTS CHECKLIST

Square   Date _____ Age ___ Initial ___ Initial ___

Truckers   Date _____ Age ___ Initial ___ Initial ___

Two Half Hitches   Date _____ Age ___ Initial ___ Initial ___

Bowline   Date _____ Age ___ Initial ___ Initial ___

Slip   Date _____ Age ___ Initial ___ Initial ___

_____ Date _____ Age ___ Initial ___ Initial ___

_____ Date _____ Age ___ Initial ___ Initial ___

_____ Date _____ Age ___ Initial ___ Initial ___

NOTES

You may not think this is all that important. But, wait until you ask one of the kids to tie your 120 year-old grandfather clock to their truck and deliver it to your new retirement condo.

13

Knots

MEMORIES

_____
_____
_____
_____
_____
_____
_____
_____
_____
_____
_____
_____
_____
_____
_____
_____
_____
_____
_____
_____
_____
_____
_____
_____
_____
_____

Laundry

Here's a sign I saw in a friend's laundry room:
"Ring bell for maid service...if no one answers...do it yourself!"

LAUNDRY CHECKLIST

Sort Clothes   Date _____ Age ___ Initial ___ Initial ___

Learn Washer and Dryer Settings   Date _____ Age ___ Initial ___ Initial ___

Use Detergents and Bleach   Date _____ Age ___ Initial ___ Initial ___

Treat Stains   Date _____ Age ___ Initial ___ Initial ___

Clean Lint Filter   Date _____ Age ___ Initial ___ Initial ___

_____   Date _____ Age ___ Initial ___ Initial ___

_____   Date _____ Age ___ Initial ___ Initial ___

_____   Date _____ Age ___ Initial ___ Initial ___

NOTES

I heard about a college freshman that destroyed the majority of his wardrobe by putting it all in the washer at the same time and dumping in a gallon of bleach. Ouch!   A really expensive lesson. Enough said.

14

Laundry

MEMORIES

_____
_____
_____
_____
_____
_____
_____
_____
_____
_____
_____
_____
_____
_____
_____
_____
_____
_____
_____
_____
_____

Lawn and Landscaping

My mom gave me this warning when I was growing up:
"Beware of landscapers who drive Rolls Royce pickup trucks."

LAWN AND LANDSCAPING CHECKLIST

Mowing	Date _____	Age ___	Initial ___	Initial ___
Edging	Date _____	Age ___	Initial ___	Initial ___
Trimming	Date _____	Age ___	Initial ___	Initial ___
Raking	Date _____	Age ___	Initial ___	Initial ___
Watering	Date _____	Age ___	Initial ___	Initial ___
Sprinkler System	Date _____	Age ___	Initial ___	Initial ___
_____	Date _____	Age ___	Initial ___	Initial ___
_____	Date _____	Age ___	Initial ___	Initial ___
_____	Date _____	Age ___	Initial ___	Initial ___

NOTES

Watering and raking a garden or lawn can be coupled with great times to get your kids started. What's more fun than running through the sprinklers on a hot day or diving into the mountain of leaves that they build in the middle of the yard?

Over time, as they hear the roar of the motors, and observe you mowing, edging, and trimming, your kids will begin to look forward to the time you tell them they're ready for these responsibilities.

15

Lawn and Landscaping

MEMORIES

_____
_____
_____
_____
_____
_____
_____
_____
_____
_____
_____
_____
_____
_____
_____
_____
_____
_____
_____
_____
_____
_____
_____
_____
_____

Maintenance

*"What is America going to do without skilled workers...
who can build and fix things?"*
– Tara Tiger Brown
Author, "From the Death of Shop Class and America's Skilled Workforce"

MAINTENANCE CHECKLIST

Locate and Operate the Outside and Inside Water and Gas Shut-Off Valves   Date _____ Age ___ Initial ___ Initial ___

Locate and Operate Circuit Breaker   Date _____ Age ___ Initial ___ Initial ___

Replace Heater, Air Conditioner and Refrigerator Filters   Date _____ Age ___ Initial ___ Initial ___

Replace Batteries in Smoke Detector Alarm   Date _____ Age ___ Initial ___ Initial ___

Reset Display Panels   Date _____ Age ___ Initial ___ Initial ___

_____   Date _____ Age ___ Initial ___ Initial ___

_____   Date _____ Age ___ Initial ___ Initial ___

_____   Date _____ Age ___ Initial ___ Initial ___

NOTES

Think about using New Year's Day as the time to replace your smoke alarm batteries. It should be done annually and making a habit of doing it on New Year's Day is a good way to make sure it gets done.

In this day and age, almost all appliances and other electronic devices require settings, including time and date, and need to be reset when there's been a power outage.

Can't say it enough...everyone in the household at the appropriate age needs to locate and know how to operate the inside and outside water and gas shut-off valves.

16

Maintenance

MEMORIES

_____
_____
_____
_____
_____
_____
_____
_____
_____
_____
_____
_____
_____
_____
_____
_____
_____
_____
_____
_____
_____
_____
_____
_____
_____
_____
_____

Painting

"First, understand that paint tools are investments."
This Old House from Mauro Henrique
Owner of Mauro's Painting

PAINTING CHECKLIST

Spray	Date _____	Age ___	Initial ___	Initial ___
Brush	Date _____	Age ___	Initial ___	Initial ___
Roller	Date _____	Age ___	Initial ___	Initial ___
Taping	Date _____	Age ___	Initial ___	Initial ___
Care Of Equipment	Date _____	Age ___	Initial ___	Initial ___
Clean Up	Date _____	Age ___	Initial ___	Initial ___
_____	Date _____	Age ___	Initial ___	Initial ___
_____	Date _____	Age ___	Initial ___	Initial ___
_____	Date _____	Age ___	Initial ___	Initial ___

NOTES

How would you ever know that you need to tip a spray can upside down and spray for a few seconds in order to clean the nozzle for the next use if someone doesn't teach you?

The proper care of paint brushes, rollers, pans, and other equipment, including rinsing and cleaning them, saves money. Without that proper care, you'll be rebuying everything every time you want to paint.

One of the hardest things for kids to learn and one of the most valuable things you can teach them is that they're not always finished when they think that they're finished.

Painting is like that. You work hard, you're happy with the results, you're tired, and so you think your finished.

But you're not! Not until the equipment is cleaned up, put away, and ready for the next project.

17

Painting

MEMORIES

Pet Care

"Teaching responsible pet care to children is an act that pays off in dividends...routine pet chores teach children responsibility and compassion."
Fetch! Pet Care

PET CARE CHECKLIST

Prepare Food and Feed Pets   Date _____ Age ___ Initial ___ Initial ___

Exercise Pets   Date _____ Age ___ Initial ___ Initial ___

Clean Up After Pets   Date _____ Age ___ Initial ___ Initial ___

Attention and Playtime   Date _____ Age ___ Initial ___ Initial ___

Washing and Drying   Date _____ Age ___ Initial ___ Initial ___

_____   Date _____ Age ___ Initial ___ Initial ___

_____   Date _____ Age ___ Initial ___ Initial ___

_____   Date _____ Age ___ Initial ___ Initial ___

NOTES

There is probably no other area of responsibility that teaches kids more life lessons than those that come with owning a pet.

Done right, it is one of the most rewarding adventures you will ever share with your child.

18

Pet Care

MEMORIES

_____
_____
_____
_____
_____
_____
_____
_____
_____
_____
_____
_____
_____
_____
_____
_____
_____
_____
_____
_____
_____
_____
_____
_____
_____
_____
_____
_____
_____

Plumbing

"If I had my life to live over again, I'd be a plumber."
Albert Einstein

PLUMBING CHECKLIST

Replace a Sink Trap   Date _____ Age ___ Initial ___ Initial ___

Replace a Faucet   Date _____ Age ___ Initial ___ Initial ___

Cut and Couple Pipe and PVC   Date _____ Age ___ Initial ___ Initial ___

Use a Pipe Wrench   Date _____ Age ___ Initial ___ Initial ___

Caulking   Date _____ Age ___ Initial ___ Initial ___

Use Plumbers Tape   Date _____ Age ___ Initial ___ Initial ___

_____   Date _____ Age ___ Initial ___ Initial ___

_____   Date _____ Age ___ Initial ___ Initial ___

_____   Date _____ Age ___ Initial ___ Initial ___

NOTES

Plumbing is another one of those areas that can lead to a full time career for your child.

My guess is that most plumbers end up in their field as a result of being introduced to it when they were young or working alongside of someone that made their living that way.

19

Plumbing

MEMORIES

Safety

"Too important..no jokes...no quotes."

SAFETY CHECKLIST

Know When and How to Call 911	Date _____	Age ___	Initial ___	Initial ___
Learn CPR	Date _____	Age ___	Initial ___	Initial ___
Learn the Heimlich Maneuver	Date _____	Age ___	Initial ___	Initial ___
Know Where the First Aid Kit is	Date _____	Age ___	Initial ___	Initial ___
Learn to Swim	Date _____	Age ___	Initial ___	Initial ___
Learn Gun and Ammunition Safety	Date _____	Age ___	Initial ___	Initial ___
Safe and Secure Medicine Storage	Date _____	Age ___	Initial ___	Initial ___
_____	Date _____	Age ___	Initial ___	Initial ___
_____	Date _____	Age ___	Initial ___	Initial ___
_____	Date _____	Age ___	Initial ___	Initial ___

NOTES

PLEASE, PLEASE, PLEASE PAY ATTENTION.

This page can be the difference between life and death.

Do whatever is necessary to teach your children these basic life skills.

20

Safety

MEMORIES

_____
_____
_____
_____
_____
_____
_____
_____
_____
_____
_____
_____
_____
_____
_____
_____
_____
_____
_____
_____
_____
_____
_____
_____
_____

Sewing and Mending

"Sewing is a fun and creative endeavor to take on, especially with your kids. Children of any age can learn some form of sewing that can get them on the path to eventually making their own complex projects and clothing."

wikihow.com – teach a child to sew

SEWING AND MENDING CHECKLIST

Thread a Needle   Date _____ Age ___ Initial ___ Initial ___

Sew on a Button   Date _____ Age ___ Initial ___ Initial ___

Stitch a Hem   Date _____ Age ___ Initial ___ Initial ___

Mend a Hole   Date _____ Age ___ Initial ___ Initial ___

_____ Date _____ Age ___ Initial ___ Initial ___

_____ Date _____ Age ___ Initial ___ Initial ___

_____ Date _____ Age ___ Initial ___ Initial ___

NOTES

If you're accomplished at using a sewing machine, or you're a champion quilter, or if you know how to knit, embroider, or crochet, do all you can to pass on your skills to your children.

In any event, don't let your kids leave home without knowing how to do at least the few things above.

Think about this: If they have to come home for you to sew on a button, they're probably going to bring four bags of laundry for you to do as well.. Nobody wants that!

21

Sewing and Mending

MEMORIES

_____
_____
_____
_____
_____
_____
_____
_____
_____
_____
_____
_____
_____
_____
_____
_____
_____
_____
_____
_____
_____
_____
_____
_____
_____
_____
_____

Small Appliances

"Teaching your children cooking with appliances should be fun for both of you. By making them feel useful, you're also helping to build their self-confidence."
KidsCookingActivities.com – 2018

SMALL APPLIANCES CHECKLIST

Toaster and Toaster Oven   Date _____ Age ___ Initial ___ Initial ___

Blender and Food Processor   Date _____ Age ___ Initial ___ Initial ___

Mixer   Date _____ Age ___ Initial ___ Initial ___

Crock Pot and Insta-Pot   Date _____ Age ___ Initial ___ Initial ___

_____   Date _____ Age ___ Initial ___ Initial ___

_____   Date _____ Age ___ Initial ___ Initial ___

_____   Date _____ Age ___ Initial ___ Initial ___

NOTES

These are actually some of the first things you're going to buy for your kids when they move out on their own.

Make sure that when they unpack them it won't be the first time they've ever used them.

22

Small Appliances

MEMORIES

_____
_____
_____
_____
_____
_____
_____
_____
_____
_____
_____
_____
_____
_____
_____
_____
_____
_____
_____
_____
_____
_____
_____
_____
_____

Time Management

"The more fun you make time management for your kids, the easier it will be to get them to understand time's importance and how to manage that constantly ticking clock."
–Apryl Duncan – Author, Very Well Family

TIME MANAGEMENT CHECKLIST

Setting And Waking To Alarm Clock   Date _____ Age ___ Initial ___ Initial ___

Use A Calendar Or Day Planner   Date _____ Age ___ Initial ___ Initial ___

Follow A Daily Schedule   Date _____ Age ___ Initial ___ Initial ___

Do Homework And Chores On Time   Date _____ Age ___ Initial ___ Initial ___

Be On Time All Of The Time   Date _____ Age ___ Initial ___ Initial ___

_____   Date _____ Age ___ Initial ___ Initial ___

_____   Date _____ Age ___ Initial ___ Initial ___

_____   Date _____ Age ___ Initial ___ Initial ___

NOTES

If you're always 15 minutes early, you'll never be late.

Plan ahead and make sure you have enough time to be on time all the time.

23

Time Management

MEMORIES

(You get to customize)

_____

_____ CHECKLIST

_____ Date _____ Age ___ Initial ___ Initial ___

_____ Date _____ Age ___ Initial ___ Initial ___

_____ Date _____ Age ___ Initial ___ Initial ___

_____ Date _____ Age ___ Initial ___ Initial ___

_____ Date _____ Age ___ Initial ___ Initial ___

_____ Date _____ Age ___ Initial ___ Initial ___

_____ Date _____ Age ___ Initial ___ Initial ___

Date _____ Age ___ Initial ___ Initial ___

NOTES

_____

_____

_____

_____

_____

27

MEMORIES

_____

(You get to customize)

CHECKLIST

_____

_____ Date _____ Age ___ Initial ___ Initial ___

_____ Date _____ Age ___ Initial ___ Initial ___

_____ Date _____ Age ___ Initial ___ Initial ___

_____ Date _____ Age ___ Initial ___ Initial ___

_____ Date _____ Age ___ Initial ___ Initial ___

_____ Date _____ Age ___ Initial ___ Initial ___

_____ Date _____ Age ___ Initial ___ Initial ___

_____ Date _____ Age ___ Initial ___ Initial ___

NOTES

_____

_____

_____

_____

_____

26

_____

MEMORIES

_____

(You get to customize)

_____ CHECKLIST

_____ Date _____ Age ___ Initial ___ Initial ___

_____ Date _____ Age ___ Initial ___ Initial ___

_____ Date _____ Age ___ Initial ___ Initial ___

_____ Date _____ Age ___ Initial ___ Initial ___

_____ Date _____ Age ___ Initial ___ Initial ___

_____ Date _____ Age ___ Initial ___ Initial ___

_____ Date _____ Age ___ Initial ___ Initial ___

_____ Date _____ Age ___ Initial ___ Initial ___

NOTES

_____

_____

_____

_____

_____

_____

24

_____

MEMORIES

_____
_____
_____
_____
_____
_____
_____
_____
_____
_____
_____
_____
_____
_____
_____
_____
_____
_____
_____
_____
_____
_____
_____

_____

(You get to customize)

_____ # CHECKLIST

_____   Date _____ Age ___ Initial ___ Initial ___

_____   Date _____ Age ___ Initial ___ Initial ___

_____   Date _____ Age ___ Initial ___ Initial ___

_____   Date _____ Age ___ Initial ___ Initial ___

_____   Date _____ Age ___ Initial ___ Initial ___

_____   Date _____ Age ___ Initial ___ Initial ___

_____   Date _____ Age ___ Initial ___ Initial ___

     Date _____ Age ___ Initial ___ Initial ___

NOTES

_____

_____

_____

_____

_____

25

_____

MEMORIES

_____
_____
_____
_____
_____
_____
_____
_____
_____
_____
_____
_____
_____
_____
_____
_____
_____
_____
_____
_____
_____
_____
_____

Certificate of Accomplishment

On this _____ day of _____ in the year of _____

Signatures

Disclaimer

I'm a really "keep it simple" kind of guy. I was hoping I could just share this guide with you and that you'd find it helpful. Turns out I'm supposed to write a disclaimer.

Now, if you watch television you've most likely seen lots of ads from pharmaceutical companies trying to get you to try their latest and greatest brand new miracle pill. They tell you the clinical name of it, (which I can never pronounce), followed by the "disclaimer" and the dreaded "POSSIBLE SIDE EFFECTS".

Here are the actual "possible side effects" from a well-known drug which shall remain nameless:

Quote: "Do not take this drug if you are allergic to it or any of its ingredients. Tell your doctor if you get a skin rash or hives, have difficulty breathing, swelling of your face, lips, tongue or throat or experience mood or behavior changes, anxiety, panic attacks, trouble sleeping, or if you feel impulsive, irritable, agitated, hostile, aggressive, restless, hyperactive, depressed, or have thoughts about suicide or hurting yourself, or if you have blurred vision, tunnel vision, eye pain or swelling, or see halos around lights or experience agitation, hallucinations, fever, fast heart rate, overactive reflexes, nausea, vomiting, diarrhea, loss of coordination, fainting, headache, confusion, slurred speech, severe weakness, feeling unsteady, very stiff muscles, high fever, sweating, confusion, fast or uneven heartbeats, tremors, feeling like you might pass out or burning in your eyes, skin pain, red or purple skin rash, blistering and peeling, yawning, strange dreams, upset stomach, loss of appetite, dry mouth, hot flashes, changes in weight or appetite, stuffy nose, sinus pain, drowsiness or slow breathing and can cause other dangerous side effects or death." Unquote

ARE YOU KIDDING ME? All of that from taking one itty-bitty pill? If I took one of those pills, I'd be afraid that my next child would be born with webbed feet and a third eye right in the middle of their forehead.

However, I've been told that THIS IS REAL IMPORTANT FOR ME TO TELL YOU:

"IF YOU HAVE ANY OF THE SYMPTOMS LISTED IN THIS GUIDE, YOU NEED TO SEEK IMMEDIATE MEDICAL HELP." There…I said it!

HERE'S MY DISCLAIMER

The only side effects you will experience from using this guide are positive ones. If you cut yourself, you're going to appreciate the life skills you learned about using a first aid kit. If you're home alone and you get hungry, you'll be glad you went through the cooking checklist.

If you have nausea and vomiting, or you have diarrhea you're going to be glad that you know how to keep your toilet working right. If you're irritable, agitated, hostile, aggressive, restless or hyperactive, you're going be grateful that you know how to use a hammer so you can beat the snot out of a nearby tree stump.

This guide is full of beneficial side effects.